Todd Whichello

Better Guitar With.

Rockschool

GW00419440

Welcome To Debut Guitar

Welcome to the Rockschool Debut guitar pack. The book and CD contain everything needed to play guitar in this grade. In the book you will find the exam scores in both standard guitar notation and TAB. The accompanying CD has full stereo mixes of each tune, backing tracks to play along with for practice, tuning notes and spoken two bar count-ins to each piece. Handy tips on playing the pieces and the marking schemes can be found in the Guru's Guide on page 14. If you have any queries about this or any other Rockschool exam, please call us on **0845 460 4747**, email us at *info@rockschool.co.uk* or visit our website *www.rockschool.co.uk*. Good luck!

Please note that the exams offered at Debut are newly accredited entry level exams. This book now supersedes all earlier editions containing performance pieces only. These books remain valid however, and users may download the additional tests from *www.rockschool.co.uk*. Please also note that these newly accredited exams have a different marking scheme to other exams in this series. Please refer to the tables on page 15.

Entry Level Techniques In Debut

The nine Rockschool grades are divided into four levels. These levels correspond to the levels of the Qualifications and Credit Framework (QCF) introduced in early 2010. Further details about the QCF can be found at: *www.ofqual.gov.uk*. Details of all of Rockschool's accredited qualifications can be found at: *www.accreditedqualifications.org.uk*.

Debut Guitar is part of the Entry Level. This Level is for players who are just starting out and who are looking to acquire the basic skills of performing and musicianship.

Debut: a player of Debut standard should be able to play up to 20 bars of music in 4/4 time, using simple first position melodies composed of whole, half and quarter notes and associated rests, as well as a range of basic first position chords. The pieces very often use open strings and melodies move mainly between adjacent strings.

The Debut Guitar Exam

There are **two** types of exam that can be taken using this pack: a Grade Exam and a Performance Certificate.

Debut Guitar Grade Exam: this is for players who want to develop performance and technical skills

Players wishing to enter for a Debut Guitar grade exam need to prepare **three** pieces. In addition you must prepare the technical exercises in the book, undertake a sight reading test, take an ear test and answer general musicianship questions. Samples of these tests are printed in the book along with audio examples on the CD.

Debut Guitar Performance Certificate: this is for players who want to focus on performing in a range of styles

To enter for your Debut Guitar Performance Certificate you play pieces only. You can choose any **five** of the six tunes printed in this book.

Guitar Notation Explained

THE MUSICAL STAVE shows pitches and rhythms and is divided by lines into bars. Pitches are named after the first seven letters of the alphabet.

TABLATURE graphically represents the guitar fingerboard. Each horizontal line represents a string, and each number represents a fret.

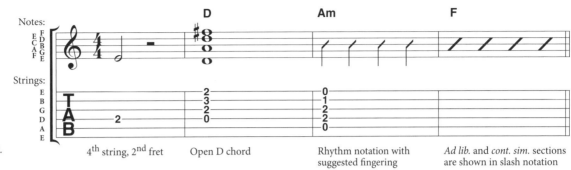

4th string, 2nd fret   Open D chord   Rhythm notation with suggested fingering   *Ad lib.* and *cont. sim.* sections are shown in slash notation

Definitions For Special Guitar Notation

HAMMER ON: Pick the lower note, then sound the higher note by fretting it without picking.

PULL OFF: Pick the higher note then sound the lower note by lifting the finger without picking.

SLIDE: Pick the first note, then slide to the next with the same finger.

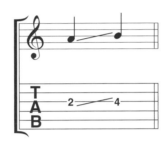

STRING BENDS: Pick the first note then bend (or release the bend) to the pitch indicated in brackets.

GLISSANDO: A small slide off of a note toward the end of its rhythmic duration. Do not slide 'into' the following note – subsequent notes should be repicked.

VIBRATO: Vibrate the note by bending and releasing the string smoothly and continuously.

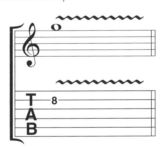

TRILL: Rapidly alternate between the two bracketed notes by hammering on and pulling off.

NATURAL HARMONICS: Lightly touch the string above the indicated fret then pick to sound a harmonic.

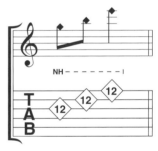

PINCHED HARMONICS: Bring the thumb of the picking hand into contact with the string immediately after the pick.

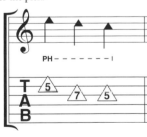

PICK HAND TAP: Strike the indicated note with a finger from the picking hand. Usually followed by a pull off.

FRET HAND TAP: As pick hand tap, but use fretting hand. Usually followed by a pull off or hammer on.

QUARTER TONE BEND: Pick the note indicated and bend the string up by a quarter tone.

PRE-BENDS: Before picking the note, bend the string from the fret indicated between the staves, to the equivalent pitch indicated in brackets in the TAB

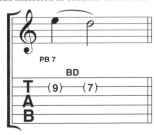

WHAMMY BAR BEND: Use the whammy bar to bend notes to the pitches indicated in brackets in the TAB

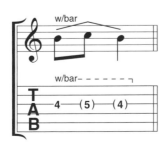

D.%. al Coda

D.C. al Fine

• Go back to the sign (%), then play until the bar marked *To Coda* ⊕ then skip to the section marked ⊕ *Coda*.

• Go back to the beginning of the song and play until the bar marked *Fine* (end).

• Repeat bars between signs.

• When a repeated section has different endings, play the first ending only the first time and the second ending only the second time.

Bean Scent

Hussein Boon

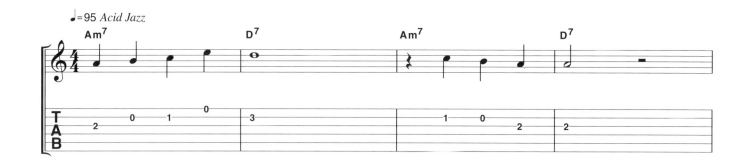

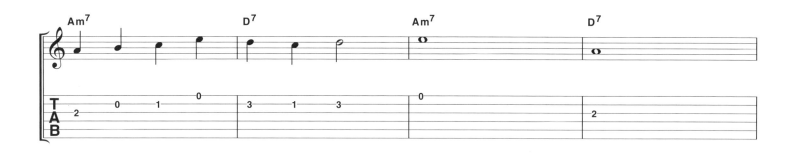

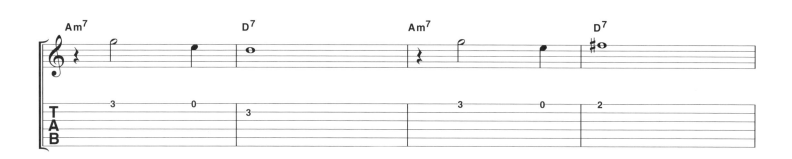

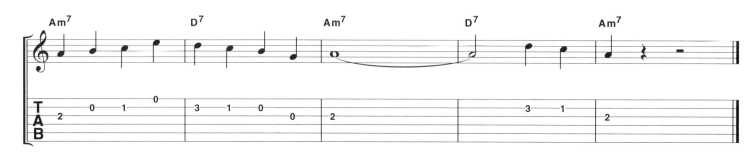

What's Your Game?

Alison Rayner

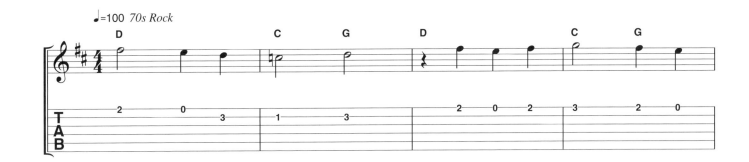

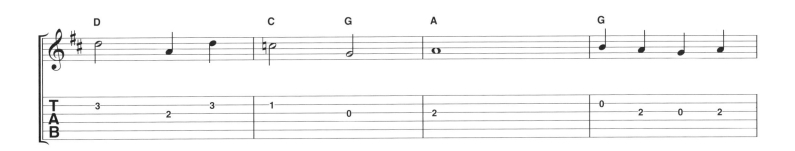

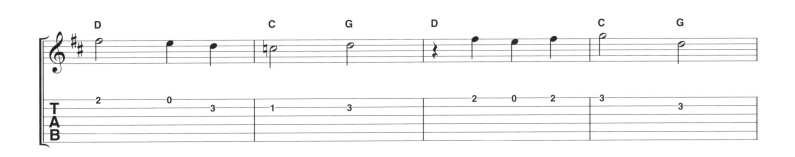

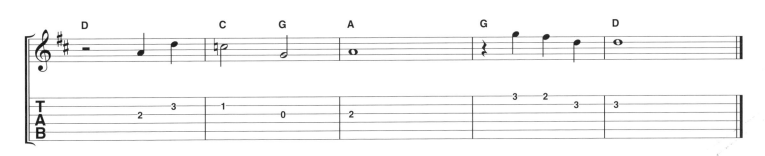

Paisley On My Mind

Joe Bennett

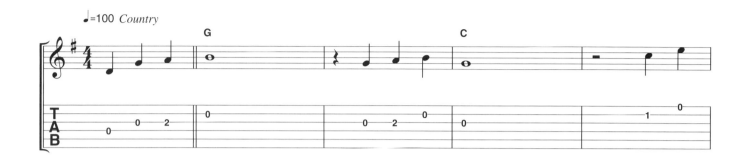

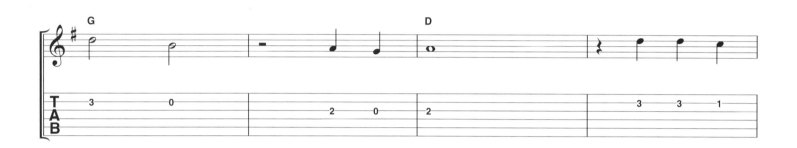

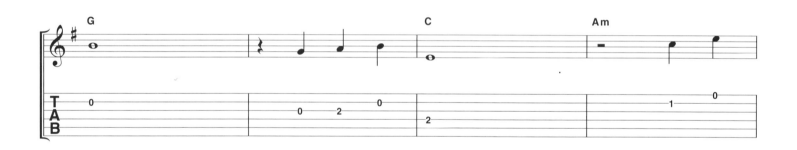

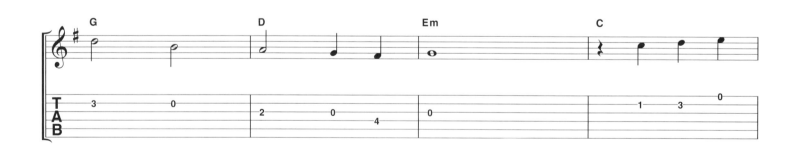

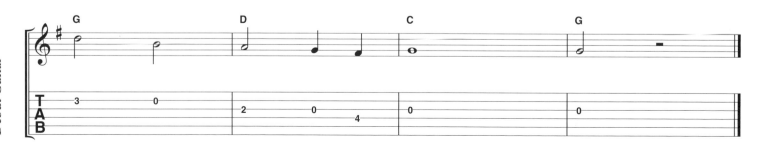

Buddy

Deirdre Cartwright

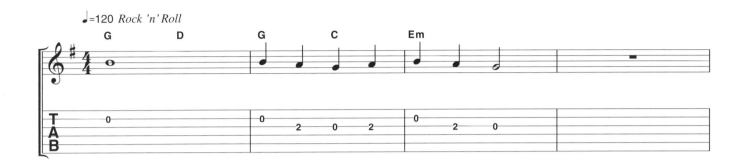

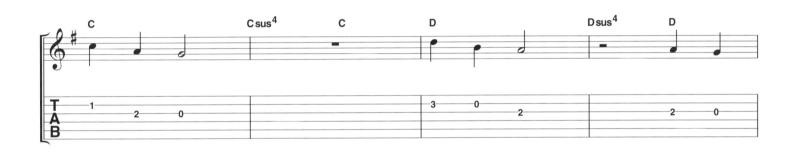

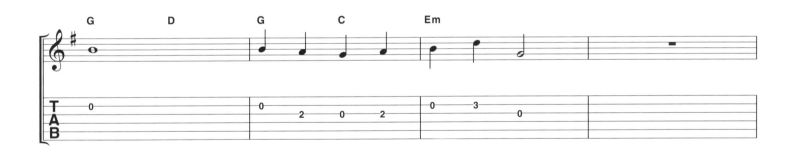

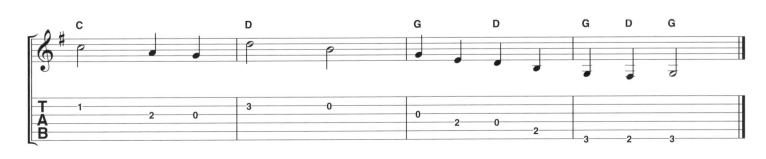

Debut Guitar

Detroit Spinna

Adrian York

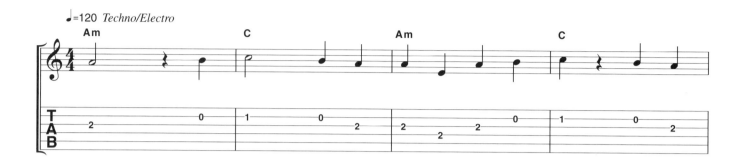

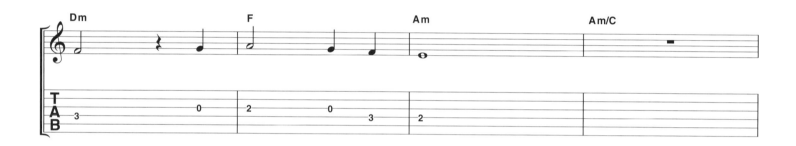

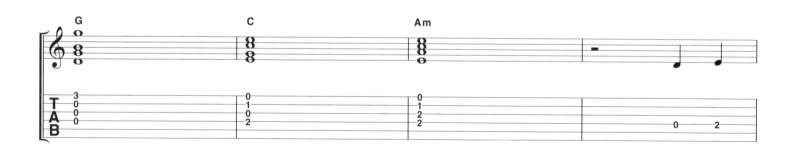

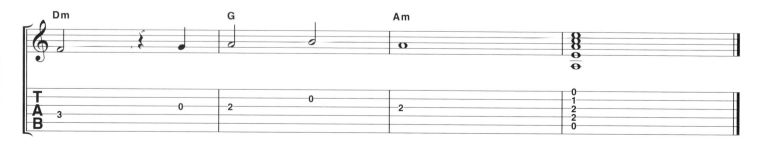

Ruby

Deirdre Cartwright

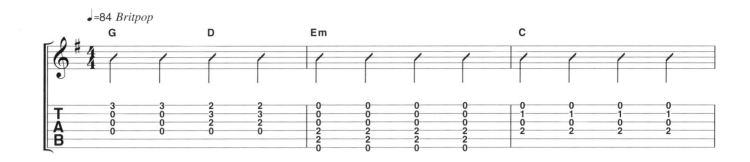

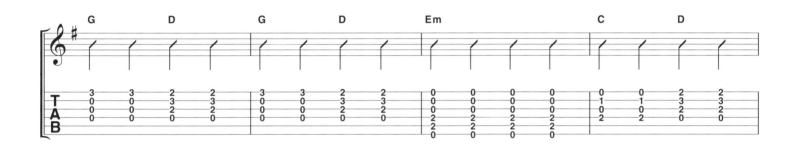

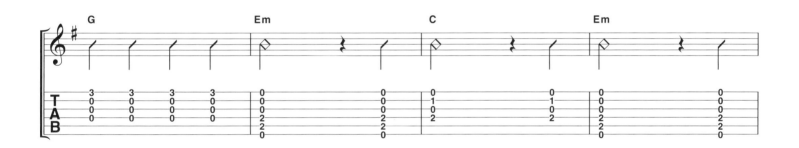

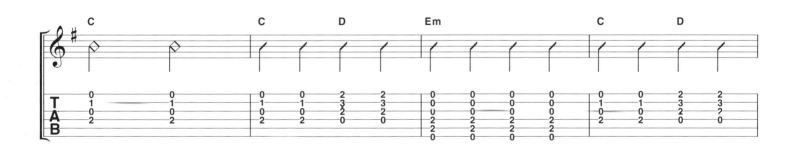

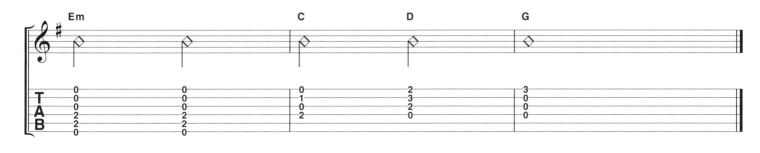

Debut Guitar

Technical Exercises

In this section, the examiner will ask you to play a selection of exercises drawn from each of the three groups shown below. Groups A and B contain examples of the kinds of scales and chords you can use when playing the pieces. In Group C you will be asked to prepare the exercise and play it to the CD backing track. You do not need to memorise the exercises (and you can use the book in the exam) but the examiner will be looking for the speed of your response. The examiner will also give credit for the level of your musicality.

Groups A and B should be prepared in the keys directed.
Groups A and B should be played at ♩ = 80. The examiner will give you this tempo in the exam.

Group A: Scales

1. E minor & A minor pentatonic. E minor pentatonic example shown

Group B: Chords

1. Open position chords. The chords shown below should be played as a continuous exercise

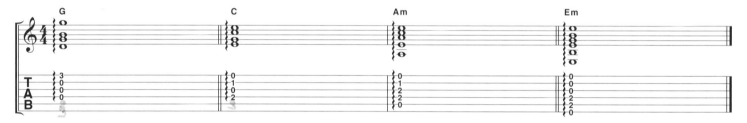

Group C: Riff

In the exam you will be asked to play the following riff to the backing track on the CD. The riff shown in bar 1 should be played in the same shape in bars 2–4. The root note of the pattern to be played is shown in the music in each of the subsequent three bars. The tempo is ♩ = 70.

Sight Reading

Printed below is the type of sight reading test you are likely to encounter in the exam. The piece will be composed in the style of either rock or blues. The examiner will allow you 90 seconds to prepare it and will set the tempo for you on a metronome. The tempo is ♩ =60.

Ear Tests

There are two ear tests in this grade. The examiner will play each test to you on CD. One example of each type of test you will be given in the exam is printed below.

Test 1: Rhythmic Recall

You will be asked to play back the given two bar rhythm on the open bottom E string of your guitar. You will hear the rhythm played twice with a drum backing. There will then be a short break for you to practise the test and then the test will recommence and you will play the rhythm to the drum backing. This test is continuous. The tempo is ♩=90.

Test 2: Melodic Recall

You will be asked to play back on your guitar a simple melody of not more than two bars composed from the first three notes of the E minor pentatonic scale (E, G and A). This will be in the same rhythm as Test 1 above. You will be given the tonic note and told the starting note and you will hear the test twice with a drum backing. There will then be a short break for you to practise the test and then the test will recommence. You will play the melody with the drum backing. This test is continuous. The tempo is ♩=90.

General Musicianship Questions

You will be asked five General Musicianship Questions at the end of the exam. The examiner will ask questions based on pieces you have played in the exam. Some of the theoretical topics can be found in the Technical Exercises.

Topics:

i)   Music theory
ii)   Knowledge of your instrument

The music theory questions will cover recognition of the following at this grade:

    Note Pitches
    Note Values
    Time Signatures

Knowledge of parts of the guitar:

    Fretboard, neck, body, tuning pegs, nut, pickups, bridge, pickup selectors, scratchplate and jack socket

Questions on all these topics will be based on pieces played by you in the exam. Tips on how to approach this part of the exam can be found on the Rockschool website: *www.rockschool.co.uk.*

The Guru's Guide To Debut Guitar

This section contains some handy hints compiled by Rockschool's Guitar Guru to help you get the most out of the performance pieces. Do feel free to adapt the tunes to suit your playing style. Remember, these tunes are your chance to show your musical imagination and personality.

The TAB fingerings are suggestions only. Feel free to use different neck positions as they suit you. Please also note that any solos featured in the full mixes are not meant to be indicative of the standard required for the grade.

Debut Guitar Tunes

Rockschool tunes help you play the hit tunes you enjoy. The pieces have been written by top pop and rock composers and players according to style specifications drawn up by Rockschool.

The tunes printed here fall into two categories. The first category can be called the 'contemporary mainstream' and features current styles in today's charts. The second category of pieces consists of 'roots styles', those classic grooves and genres which influence every generation of performers.

CD full mix track 1, backing track 8: Bean Scent

A track in the style of Acid Jazz, a form of funk music that had its heyday in the early 1990s with bands such as Freak Power and early Jamiroquai. The main theme is played in quarter notes for the most part with some half and whole notes. Watch out for the rests at the start of bars 3, 9, 11 and 15 and make sure that you give the quarter and whole notes their full value.

Composer: Hussein Boon.

CD full mix track 2, backing track 9: What's Your Game?

A 70s rock piece after the manner of Black Sabbath. The part consists of half and quarter notes and again watch for the quarter note rests at the beginning of bars 3, 11 and 15. The tempo is quite brisk so make sure that you don't rush the half notes and to give them their full value.

Composer: Alison Rayner.

CD full mix track 3, backing track 10: Paisley On My Mind

This country tune has a three note lead in to the main theme and is deceptively simple in appearance. The use of whole notes followed by rests in the following bars make this song an exercise in counting, particularly as the rests in bars 5, 7 and 13 are half note rests and not quarter notes as in bars 3, 9, 11 and 17, so make sure you give the whole notes their correct value.

Composer: Joe Bennett.

CD full mix track 4, backing track 11: Buddy

A brisk rock 'n' roll song evoking the style of Buddy Holly. The part consists of quarter and half notes and mixes up whole notes and rests which again make this piece a valuable exercise in counting. Watch out for the ending as this is quite tricky and will require plenty of practice.

Composer: Deirdre Cartwright

CD full mix track 5, backing track 12: Detroit Spinna

A techno/electro piece again taken at a brisk pace. The part mixes up quarter and half notes; make sure you observe the rests which come in different places in the bar. The three chords in bars 9-11 should be played crisply and evenly, as should the final A minor chord at the end.

Composer: Adrian York.

CD full mix track 6, backing track 13: Ruby

This laid back guitar pop piece consists wholly of chords played for the first eight bars in an even, four-to-the-bar rhythm. The second half of the song sees this rhythm mixed up with a rest on the third beat of the next three bars. The main points to watch out for are those bars which have two chords in them, particularly in the first half of the piece, so make sure that the movement between chords is fluent and that each note is clearly picked where indicated. You will notice that the G chord is notated for the top four strings only.

Composer: Deirdre Cartwright.

CD Musicians:

Guitars: Deirdre Cartwright
Bass: Henry Thomas
Drums: George Gavin
Keyboards and programming: Alastair Gavin

Debut Guitar Marking Scheme

The table below shows the marking scheme for the Debut Guitar grade exam. Please note that all successful candidates will be certificated as achieving a pass only.

ELEMENT	PASS
Piece 1	13 out of 20
Piece 2	13 out of 20
Piece 3	13 out of 20
Technical Exercises	11 out of 15
Sight Reading	6 out of 10
Ear Tests	6 out of 10
General Musicianship Questions	3 out of 5
Total Marks	**Pass: 65%+**

The table below shows the marking scheme for the Debut Guitar Performance Certificate. Please note that all successful candidates will be certificated as achieving a pass only.

ELEMENT	PASS
Piece 1	14 out of 20
Piece 2	14 out of 20
Piece 3	14 out of 20
Piece 4	14 out of 20
Piece 5	14 out of 20
Total Marks	**Pass: 70%+**

Entering Rockschool Exams

Entering a Rockschool exam is easy. Please read through these instructions carefully before filling in the exam entry form. Information on current exam fees can be obtained from Rockschool by ringing **0845 460 4747** or by logging on to our website *www.rockschool.co.uk*.

• You should enter for your exam when you feel ready.

• You can enter for any one of three examination periods. These are shown below with their closing dates.

PERIOD	DURATION	CLOSING DATE
Period A	1st February to 15th March	1st December
Period B	1st May to 31st July	1st April
Period C	23rd October to 15th December	1st October

These dates will apply from 1st September 2006 until further notice

• Please complete the form giving the information required. Please fill in the type and level of exam, the instrument, along with the period and year. Finally, fill in the fee box with the appropriate amount. You can obtain up to date information on all Rockschool exam fees from the website: *www.rockschool.co.uk*. You should send this form with a cheque or postal order (payable to **Rockschool**) to the address shown on the order form. **Please also indicate on the form whether or not you would like to receive notification via email.**

• Applications received after the expiry of the closing date may be accepted subject to the payment of an additional fee.

• When you enter an exam you will receive from Rockschool an acknowledgement letter or email containing a copy of our exam regulations.

• Rockschool will allocate your entry to a centre and you will receive notification of the exam, showing a date, location and time as well as advice of what to bring to the centre. We endeavour to give you four weeks' notice of your exam.

• You should inform Rockschool of any cancellations or alterations to the schedule as soon as you can as it is usually not possible to transfer entries from one centre, or one period, to another without the payment of an additional fee.

• Please bring your music book and CD to the exam. You may not use photocopied music, nor the music used by someone else in another exam. The examiner will sign each book during each examination. You may be barred from taking an exam if you use someone else's music.

• You should aim to arrive for your Debut exam fifteen minutes before the time stated on the schedule. You should use this time to tune your guitar and get everything ready to take your exam.

• Each Debut grade exam is scheduled to last for 12 minutes. Each Debut performance certificate is scheduled to last 10 minutes.

• Two to three weeks after the exam you will receive a copy of the examiner's mark sheet. Every successful player will receive a Rockschool certificate of achievement.